My Inner Voice

A Woman's Journal of Self-discovery

Finding Your Voice...Being Inspired...Trusting Your Intuition...Living in the Moment

Most people already know that journaling can be a powerful tool in self-discovery and self-knowledge. Most of us know that writing in a journal can be therapeutic and meditative, as well as comforting and inspiring. But many of us still have a hard time finding time to write. And once we do have a moment, there are so many things to say, and so many ways they could be said.

Finding your voice is an essential step on the path of self-discovery. Learning to say what you mean and expressing how you really feel without censoring yourself or holding back may be one of the greatest gifts you ever give yourself. Being in touch with and accepting yourself is something that will dramatically add to the quality and vitality of your life.

This journal is full of short, guided meditations designed to stir up feelings and inspire you to write and reflect. Hopefully, as you take this journey, you'll get reacquainted with yourself and you will remember the desires that are closest to your heart. You'll get back in touch with your creative side and examine the relationships that enrich your life. You'll slow down long enough to live in each moment and breathe the air of today. Stop worrying about tomorrow, and be thankful for the blessings that surround you in this moment.

As you write in this journal, remember to trust your intuition. When you do so, you're truly listening to your voice. Believe in that voice. Trust the feelings deep in your gut. Those are the feelings that make you who you are.

"Your daily life is your temple and your religion."
—Kahlil Gibran

Contents

- Blessings
- Every Day
- Simple Pleasures
- Faith and Hope
- Peace of Mind
- Friendship
- Important People
- Motivation
- Turning Points
- Appreciation and Acceptance
- Pleasing Your Soul
- Reflections on Happiness
- Thoughts on the Future

Blessings

Take a careful look at what surrounds you...what are you thankful for? It doesn't have to be anything unusual; sometimes the greatest blessings are the things we take for granted.

"When I first open my eyes upon the morning meadows and look out upon the beautiful world, I thank God I am alive."

—Ralph Waldo Emerson

"Most humans have an almost infinite
capacity for taking things for granted."
—Aldous Huxley

"God gave you a gift of 86,400 seconds today. Have you used one to say 'thank you'?"

—William A. Ward

"A thankful heart is not only the greatest virtue, but the parent of all other virtues."

—Cicero

"Seeds of discouragement will not grow in a thankful heart."

—Anonymous

"Reflect upon your present blessings, of which every man has many; not on your past misfortunes, of which all men have some."

—Charles Dickens

"The secret of happiness is not in doing what one likes, but in liking what one has to do."
—Sir James M. Barrie

Every Day

Sometimes it's all too easy to let the days of our lives go by without appreciating the beauty of what we see and do each day. What are the things you do every day that you love? What do you look forward to when you wake up in the morning? Think about the greater purpose behind the everyday tasks that you do. What else would you like to do with your days?

_____
_____
_____
_____
_____
_____
_____
_____
_____
_____
_____
_____
_____
_____
_____
_____
_____
_____
_____

"Eden is that old-fashioned house we
dwell in every day
Without suspecting our abode until
we drive away."

—Emily Dickinson

"I thank you God for this most amazing day;
for the leaping greenly spirits of trees and a
blue true dream of sky; and for everything
which is natural which is infinite which is yes."
—e.e. cummings

"Yes, there is a Nirvanah: it is in leading your sheep to a green pasture, and in putting your child to sleep, and in writing the last line of your poem."

—Kahlil Gibran

"Write it in your heart that every day is the best day of the year."
—Ralph Waldo Emerson

"Fear less, hope more; eat less, chew more; whine less, breathe more; talk less, say more; love more, and all good things will be yours."

—Swedish proverb

"There is a time for work. And a time for love. That leaves no other time."
—Coco Chanel

"We should consider every day lost on
which we have not danced at least once."
—Friedrich Nietzsche

Simple Pleasures

What are you grateful for? Sometimes the simplest pleasures are the greatest. What are some of your favorite things? What's your favorite flower, favorite relative, or favorite restaurant? How do you pass on these simple pleasures to others?

"Is it so small a thing to have enjoyed the sun, to have lived light in the spring, to have loved, to have thought, to have done?"

—Matthew Arnold

"Simplicity is the ultimate sophistication."
—Leonardo da Vinci

"Life is not complex. We are complex. Life is simple, and the simple thing is the right thing."
—Oscar Wilde

"It is the sweet, simple things of life
which are the real ones after all."
                              —Laura Ingalls Wilder

Faith & Hope

In our darkest hours, faith and hope keep us strong. What do you have faith in? Has your faith ever been challenged? What did you learn from that experience? Write about what faith means to you. Write about times when hope was your salvation, or how you think you could help someone else through a difficult situation.

"I believe in the sun even if it isn't shining. I believe in love even when I am alone. I believe in God even when He is silent."
—World War Two refugee

"Faith is a sounder guide than reason. Reason can only go so far, but faith has no limits."
—Blaise Pascal

"Faith is not something to grasp, it is a state to grow into."
—Mahatma Gandhi

"Hope is a waking dream."
—Aristotle

"Hold your head high, stick your chest out. You can make it. It gets dark sometimes but morning comes...Keep hope alive."
—Jesse Jackson

"Faith is that quality or power by which the things that are desired become the things possessed."
—Kathryn Kuhlman

Peace of Mind

At the end of an especially stressful day, what brings you peace of mind? Do you take time out of your day for yourself? Write about how you achieve peace of mind, and what you do (or should do) to preserve it.

_____

_____

_____

_____

_____

_____

_____

_____

_____

_____

_____

_____

_____

_____

_____

_____

_____

_____

_____

_____

_____

"Nothing can bring you peace but yourself."

—Ralph Waldo Emerson

"I go by instinct...I don't worry about experience."
—Barbara Streisand

"Nowhere can man find a quieter or more untroubled retreat than in his own soul."

—Marcus Aurelius

"If there is to be any peace it will come through being, not having."

—Henry Miller

"All the troubles of life come upon us because we refuse to sit quietly for awhile each day in our rooms."
—Blaise Pascal

"There is time for everything."
—Thomas Edison

Friendship

Our friends sometimes constitute our entire world, and other times, they are a subtle but constant influence in our daily lives. Write about the amazing friends you've made in your lifetime, and about your experiences together. How have your friends helped and inspired you to become a better person? Who among your friends is consistently supportive and inspiring? Have you been an inspiration to any of your friends?

"Each friend represents a world in us, a world possibly not born until they arrive, and it is only by this meeting that a new world is born."
—Anaïs Nin

"The most called-upon prerequisite of a friend is an accessible ear."
—Maya Angelou

"They are rich who have true friends."
—Thomas Fuller

"It's the friends you can call up at 4 A.M. that matter."

—Marlene Dietrich

"If we would build on a sure founda-
tion in friendship, we must love friends
for their sake rather than for our own."
—Charlotte Brontë

Important People

Heroes can come in all shapes and sizes; sometimes, as children, our heroes seem larger than life. But some consider friends or parents to be their true heroes. Others admire movie stars and famous athletes. Who have your mentors been? Why do you admire them? Write about what you have learned from them and how they have influenced you.

"A bit of fragrance always clings to the hand that gives you roses."
—Chinese proverb

"As you get older it is harder to have heroes, but it is sort of necessary"
—Ernest Hemingway

"Example is not the main thing in influencing others. It is the only thing."
—Albert Schweitzer

"Make yourself necessary to somebody."
—Ralph Waldo Emerson

"I am my own heroine."
—Marie Bashkirtseff

Motivation

When things get tough, where does your willpower come from? What motivates you to achieve your goals? What keeps you going, even when you feel discouraged? Some say a strong will is the best tool for success. Write about the ways in which you motivate yourself, and about those who motivate you to do your best.

_____

_____

_____

_____

_____

_____

_____

_____

_____

_____

_____

_____

_____

_____

_____

_____

_____

_____

_____

"This is not a dress rehearsal. This is it."
—Tom Cunningham

"Either you reach a higher point today, or you exercise your strength in order to be able to climb higher tomorrow."
—Friedrich Nietzsche

"Anyone can have an off decade."
—Larry Cole

"We should not let our fears hold us back from pursuing our hopes."
—John F. Kennedy

"I am seeking, I am striving, I am in it with all my heart."

—Vincent van Gogh

*"The journey of a thousand miles
must begin with a single step."*
−Chinese proverb

"It's a long road, but I know I'm gonna find the end."

—Bessie Smith

Turning Points

Days come and go, and somewhere along the way, things change. Sometimes change comes gradually over a long period of time, and other times, it strikes quickly. Write about the times in your life when your feelings, attitude, or outlook were forever changed. What were some of your life-changing experiences? What were your turning points?

"Change is the process by which
the future invades our lives."
—Alvin Toffler

"When you're through changing, you're through"

—Bruce Barton

"Every radical adjustment is a crisis in self-esteem: we undergo a test; we have to prove ourselves. It takes inordinate self-confidence to face drastic change without inner trembling."

—Eric Hoffer

"All is change; all yields its place and goes."
—Euripedes

Appreciation & Acceptance

Often once we gain an appreciation of our surroundings, and work toward an acceptance of life's challenges, we begin to look at the world through different eyes. What have you grown to accept? What can you now appreciate? Write about the obstacles you've overcome, and what you've learned from those experiences.

_____

_____

_____

_____

_____

_____

_____

_____

_____

_____

_____

_____

_____

_____

_____

_____

_____

_____

"The past is but the beginning of a beginning, and all that is and has been is but the twilight of the dawn."
—H.G. Wells

"The first rule is to keep an untroubled spirit. The second is to look things in the face and know them for what they are."
—Marcus Aurelius

"Possessions dwindle; I mourn their loss. But I mourn the loss of time much more, for anyone can save his purse, but none can win back lost time."
—Latin proverb

"There is no cure for birth and death save to enjoy the interval."
—George Santayana

"Arrange whatever pieces come your way."
—Virginia Woolf

Pleasing Your Soul

Do you ever take time out for yourself? Treat yourself to a long bath or a new outfit? Think about the things your soul craves. They don't have to be fancy or complex—they can be as simple as fresh linens, home-baked cookies, or the sound of rain on your window. Write about what always brings a big smile to your face—and then take some time to pamper yourself!

"If you obey all the rules, you miss all the fun."
—Katharine Hepburn

"If we go down into ourselves, we find that we possess exactly what we desire."
—Simon Weil

"There are no rules. Just follow your heart."
–Robin Williams

"I always thought I should be treated like a star."
—Madonna

"There is applause superior to that of the multitudes—one's own."
—Elizabeth Elton Smith

Reflections on Happiness

Happiness, though sometimes elusive, is what humankind struggles for. Write about the times in your life when you have been truly happy. What makes you happy? How have you tried to bring happiness to others? What do you consider to be the key to happiness?

"Happiness is when what you think, what
you say, and what you do are in harmony."
—Mahatma Gandhi

*"Knowledge of what is possible
is the beginning of happiness."*
—George Santayana

"May you have warmth in your igloo, oil in your lamp, and peace in your heart."
—Eskimo proverb

"The supreme happiness of life is
the conviction that we are loved."
—Victor Hugo

"The better part of happiness
is to wish to be what you are."
—Desiderius Erasmus

Thoughts on the Future

What do you look forward to? What are the things that you want to try or do? What dreams do you want to make a reality? What hopes and visions do you have for those who are closest to you? Write about how you envision your life in the future.

"I look forward to being older, when what you look like becomes less and less an issue and what you are is the point."

—Susan Sarandon

"An aim in life is the only fortune worth finding."
—Jacqueline Kennedy Onassis

"A dream is always simmering below the conventional surface of speech and reflection."
—George Santayana

"The only limit to our realization of tomor-
row will be our doubts of today. Let us
move forward with strong and active faith."
—Franklin Delano Roosevelt

"The future belongs to those who
believe in the beauty of their dreams."
—Eleanor Roosevelt